MICHELLE'S FULL HOUSE™ SCRAPBOOK

BY JUDY NAYER
WITH ADDITIONS BY DEBRA C. MOSTOW

A Creative Media Applications Production

SCHOLASTIC INC.
New York Toronto London Auckland Sydney

ISBN 0-590-20309-6

12 11 10 9 8 7 6 5 4 3 2 1 5 6 7 8 9/9 0/0

Printed in the U.S.A. 14

First Scholastic printing, March 1995

HI! I'm Michelle Tanner. This is my scrapbook of pictures of my family and me. Did you know I have a really big family? There's nine of us (plus Comet, our dog) all living together in one house. Sometimes we get on each other's nerves. But mostly we love having such a full house! Do you want to meet everybody? Just look inside!

D. J. (Donna Jo) TANNER

D.J. is my oldest sister. She's seventeen — ten years older than I am! D.J.'s in her last year of high school. I can't wait to be grown-up just like my big sister!

I love this picture of D.J. Doesn't she look beautiful? She's also really nice and tries to spend a lot of time with me. I'm so lucky!

Sometimes it is hard for me to believe that D.J. used to be soooo young! Boy, do I feel old.

I sure am going to miss D.J. when she goes off to college one day. Hmmm ... but maybe I'll get my own room then.

Steve was D.J.'s first *real* boyfriend. I had a very big crush on him. He and I even got married, but it was just pretend. Oh, well!

STEPHANIE TANNER

Stephanie is my middle sister. She's five years older than I am and five years younger than D.J. Sometimes being the middle kid is difficult for Stephanie.

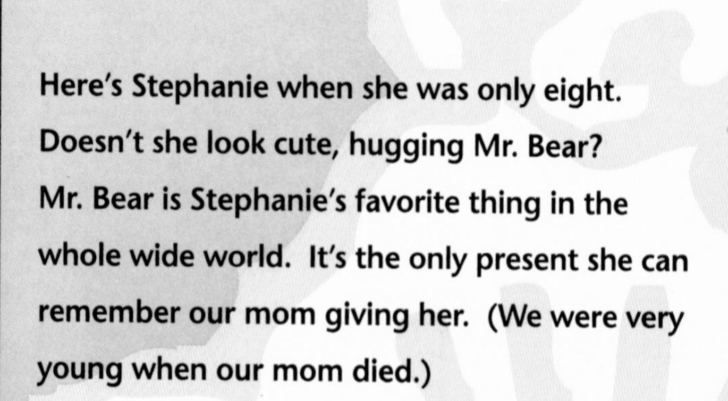

Here's Stephanie when she was only eight. Doesn't she look cute, hugging Mr. Bear? Mr. Bear is Stephanie's favorite thing in the whole wide world. It's the only present she can remember our mom giving her. (We were very young when our mom died.)

RIGHT Stephanie and D.J. used to share a room. Now Stephanie lives with me. I love having her as a roommate (most of the time).

BELOW That's Stephanie and me in the backyard with Comet. Will you get a look at what Stephanie's wearing? She sure has some very cool — and colorful — clothes.

Here's Stephanie and D.J., probably getting another one of Dad's famous lectures. Do you think they're listening?

MICHELLE TANNER
(Me)

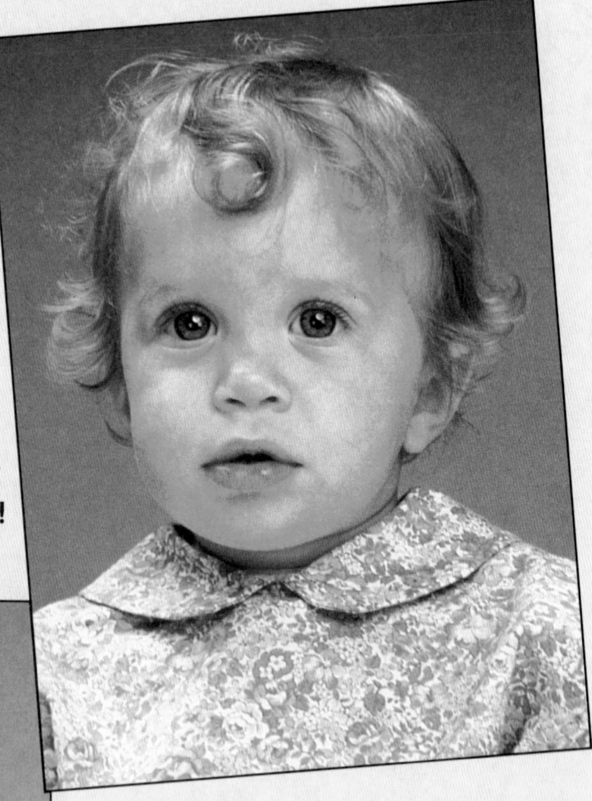

Here I am when I was just a baby.
Everyone says I was so adorable.
But I think I look a lot better with hair!

LEFT When I was little I was really bossy. I used to say things like "Watch it, Mister!" and "No way, José!" Most of the time my family thought it was really cute. But sometimes I drove them crazy!

BELOW I used to have a lot of stuffed animals! Barney the Bear was my favorite. I still have him!

I was so scared the first day of kindergarten! But my family was really nice. Dad and Uncle Joey told me everything was going to be okay and Stephanie promised to look out for me.

RIGHT Dad always knows the right things to say. And he's a good listener, too.

BELOW Who's ready for breakfast? Who's ready to go back to bed?

DANNY TANNER
(Dad)

This is my dad getting a real kick out of me. He's so easy to entertain!

I've always been Dad's "little princess." Come on, Dad, let's go!

Sometimes it's hard for my sisters and me not having a mom around. But Dad's always there for us. Whenever we have a problem we go to Dad. He always listens and helps us work it out. You should hear one of his famous "Dad talks"!

Here's Steve getting a lecture from Dad. I hope Dad won't act as goofy with my boyfriend as he did with D.J.'s.

Dad is such a neat freak! We call him "Captain Clean." He even used the names of his favorite cleaning stuff to teach me how to read. I'm sure I'm the only kid that learned, "A is for ammonia!"

JESSE KATSOPOLIS
(Uncle Jesse)

Uncle Jesse is a great musician. He has even played with the Beach Boys!

I like going shopping with Uncle Jesse. He buys us the coolest clothes!

This is one of my favorite pictures of us.

Uncle Jesse was real nervous when he first found out he and Aunt Becky were having twins. But he got the hang of it pretty quickly!

JOEY GLADSTONE

(Uncle Joey)

Uncle Joey has taught me a lot about sports. Don't we look cute in our hockey uniforms?

BELOW Uncle Joey is the funniest guy I know. And after all these years, he still can make Dad and Uncle Jesse smile.

Uncle Joey also has a serious side. And he really knows how to listen.

Uh-oh! What did Uncle Joey and the twins do now?

Some people will do anything for a laugh!

REBECCA DONALDSON-KATSOPOLIS
(Aunt Becky)

RIGHT She and Uncle Jesse are so great together!

BELOW Aunt Becky fit right into our family.

When Nicky and Alex were first born, Aunt Becky had them wear different-colored booties so she could tell them apart.

When Kenny (a boy in my class) said girls don't have "car" brains, just "doll" brains, Aunt Becky straightened me out. She helped me build a car for the Downhill Derby race. I learned girls can do anything boys can do!

D.J. would speak with Aunt Becky about Steve a lot. I hope Aunt Becky stills lives with us when I start dating!

NICHOLAS & ALEXANDER KATSOPOLIS

(Nicky & Alex)

I think Nicky and Alex look like Uncle Jesse.

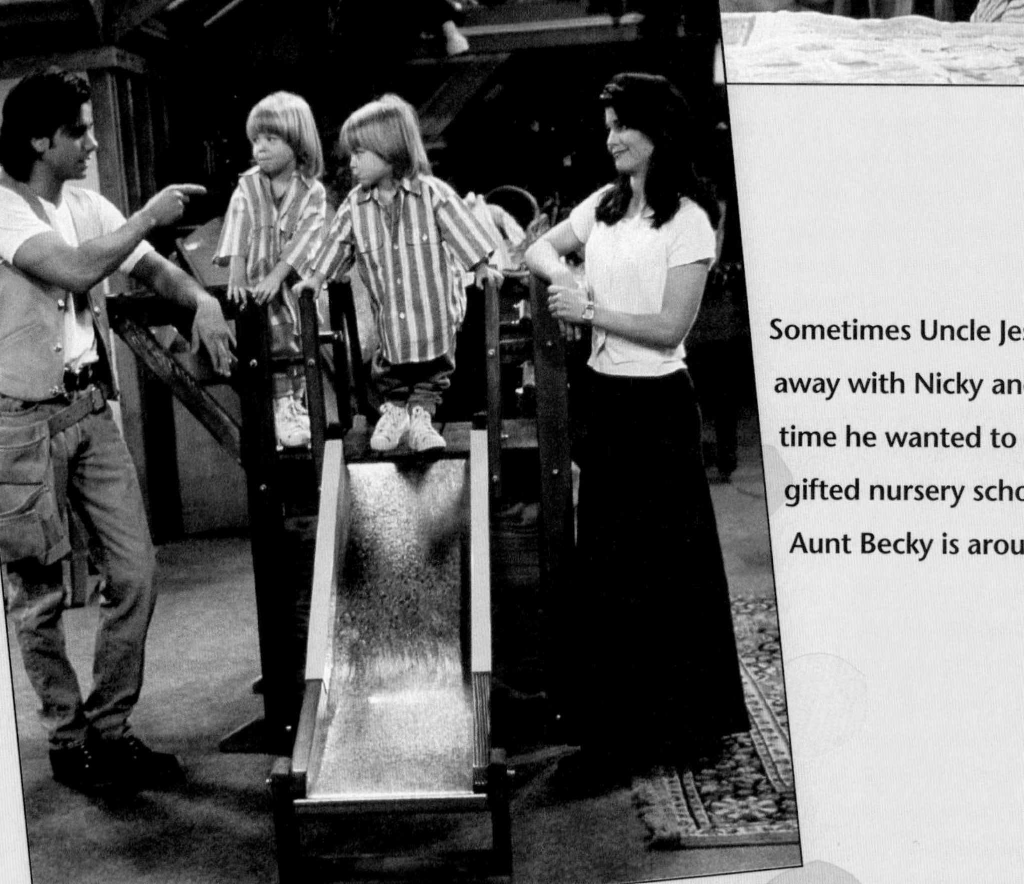

Sometimes Uncle Jesse gets carried away with Nicky and Alex. Like the time he wanted to enroll them in a gifted nursery school. Good thing Aunt Becky is around.

ABOVE Uncle Jesse loves Nicky and Alex so much. He's such a great dad!

RIGHT At first it was hard to get used to not being the baby in the family anymore. And I missed Uncle Jesse because he spent so much time with Nicky and Alex instead of with me. But now, I can't imagine living without them!

Nicky and Alex used to really misbehave. But, lately, they've been listening a lot more.

COMET

Comet is another member of our family. D.J. took this picture of us on New Year's Eve. Happy New Year, Comet! I'll never forget the time I tried one of Comet's Doggie Doodles. Yuck!

Comet's really big now, but when we got him he was just a puppy. Here he is with D.J. Isn't he cute?

RIGHT Do you know how we got Comet? We took in a lost dog, named Minnie, and she had puppies — right in our house! When we finally found Minnie's owner, he let us keep one of the puppies — Comet! (I wanted to keep them all.)

BELOW RIGHT Comet hates to sleep in his own bed. Sometimes he sleeps with D.J. or Stephanie. He's been sneaking into my bed ever since he was a puppy.

I swear, at times Comet *thinks* he's human!

AROUND THE HOUSE

A family meeting! Hey, wait, where am I?

ABOVE Uh-oh, look who's got her head stuck in the banister!

RIGHT Comet takes part in many of our family meetings. He doesn't speak much, though.

Oh, boy, what's Dad talking about now?

Uncle Joey sure acts weird sometimes!

MY SISTERS AND ME

This is my favorite picture of my sisters and me. Do you think we look alike?

I sure am glad I don't have homework like Stephanie and D.J.

All three of us took ballet lessons. And we all wore the same tutu. When D.J. and Stephanie first handed it down to me, I loved it so much I wouldn't take it off. I wore it for three days straight. I even slept in it!

MY SISTERS AND ME

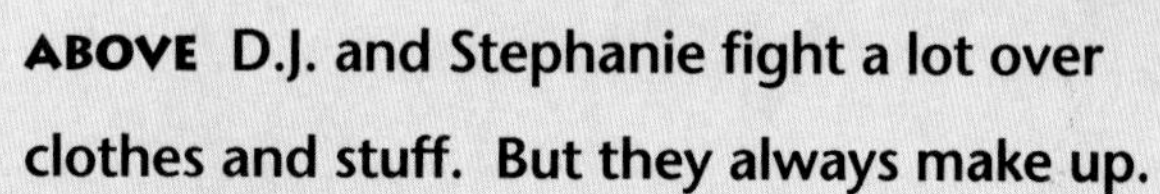

ABOVE D.J. and Stephanie fight a lot over clothes and stuff. But they always make up.

Wow! Were we ever this young?

Dad took this picture the night we came home from camp. He was so glad we were back!

ALL DRESSED UP

At Uncle Jesse and Aunt Becky's wedding, I got to be the flower girl. My dress was so beautiful!

What's happening, dude?

Who's that cutie hiding behind the mask?

NEXT PAGE I think we look just great in our tuxedos!

ONSTAGE

Here's Uncle Jesse playing rock and roll!

One time Uncle Joey appeared on *Star Search*.

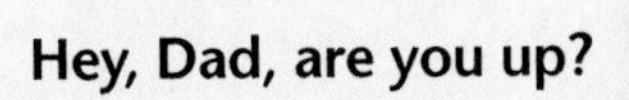

Hey, Dad, are you up?

FUNNY PICTURES

D.J. didn't think her hair looked so funny, but I did!

Someone caught Joey in his favorite spot! He says the bathtub is the only place he can get any privacy.

TOP Can you believe Dad and Uncle Joey have the nerve to make fun of Uncle Jesse? What about the shower cap Uncle Joey is wearing?

RIGHT Who is this dog and where did he come from?

Ride 'em cowboy! Yahoo!

MEMORABLE MOMENTS

I'll never forget that first day of kindergarten.

I *still* listen when Uncle Jesse speaks.

Stephanie did it again!

Can you believe I won the Downhill Derby race? When I got the trophy, I decided to share it with Aunt Becky since she was the one who helped me make the car.

MEMORABLE MOMENTS

RIGHT My sisters and I sure do have the best dad in the whole world. And let me tell you, we are not always so easy to handle.

BELOW I don't know who's cuter — the puppies or me!

I'll never forget when Uncle Jesse sang to Aunt Becky at their wedding.

The first — and last — time Uncle Jesse let Stephanie cut his hair.

FAMILY TIME

Here's a picture when Dad took us all to Hawaii. Aloha!

Good 'ol Dad is always ready for a hug.

Uncle Joey loves to feel appreciated!

No matter what, we'll always love our dad.

FULL HOUSE™